The Elves and the Shoemaker

PaRragon

Bath · New York · Singapore · Hong Kong · Cologne · Delhi · Melbourne

Notes for Parents

These **Gold Stars**® reading books encourage and support children who are learning to read.

Starting to read

• Start by reading the book aloud to your child. Take time to talk about the pictures. They often give clues about the story. The easy-to-read speech bubbles provide an excellent 'joining-in' activity.

• Over time, try to read the same book several times. Gradually, your child will want to read the book aloud with you. It helps to run your finger under the words as you say them.

• Occasionally, stop and encourage your child to continue reading aloud without you. Join in again when your child needs help. This is the next step towards helping your child become an independent reader.

• Finally, your child will be ready to read alone. Listen carefully and give plenty of praise. Remember to make reading an enjoyable experience.

Using your stickers
The fun colour stickers in the centre of the book and fold-out scene board at the back will help your child re-enact parts of the story, again and again.

Remember these four stages:
- Read the story **to** your child.
- Read the story **with** your child.
- Encourage your child to read **to you**.
- Listen to your child read **alone**.

Once upon a time there was a shoemaker and his wife. The shoemaker worked very hard. But they were very poor.

One day, all the shoemaker had left was one small piece of leather.

"I will only be able to make one pair of shoes," said the shoemaker.

The shoemaker cut out a pair of shoes.
He left them on his workbench to sew
the next morning.

They are perfect!

The next morning, the shoemaker was surprised.
He found a pair of shoes on his workbench.
They were perfect. But the shoemaker did not
know who had sewn them.   11

That day, a rich lady came into the shop and put on the shoes.

"They are a perfect fit," said the rich lady.

She gave the shoemaker a big bag of money.

Now the shoemaker had money to buy leather for two pairs of shoes.

The shoemaker cut out two pairs of shoes.
He left them on his workbench to sew
the next morning.

The next morning, the shoemaker was surprised.

He found two pairs of shoes on his workbench.

"They are perfect!" said his wife.   15

That day, a rich man came into the shop.

He bought both pairs of shoes.

He gave the shoemaker two big bags of money.

The shoemaker was very happy.

Now he had enough money to buy leather

to make four pairs of shoes.

I am very happy.

Night after night, the same thing happened. The shoemaker cut out the leather and left it on the workbench. Every morning he found perfect shoes in its place.

But the shoemaker still did not know who was sewing the shoes.

One night, the shoemaker and his wife hid
in the workshop.
They waited to see who would come.

At midnight, two tiny elves ran in.

Their clothes were very old.

They jumped onto the workbench and started to sew. They did not stop until the last shoe was made.

"We must make the elves a present," said
the shoemaker to his wife.
So the shoemaker made two pairs of tiny shoes.
His wife made two tiny suits.
It took them a very long time.

One night, they left the shoes and suits on the workbench. Then they hid and waited to see what would happen.

At midnight, the two tiny elves ran in.
They jumped up onto the workbench.
They were surprised to see the tiny clothes
and shoes.

They put on their new clothes and shoes.

They were very happy.

They liked the clothes and shoes.

The shoemaker and his wife never saw the elves again. But they did not mind. The elves had brought them good luck.

From that day on, the shoemaker worked harder than ever.

And they were never poor again.

Read and Say

How many of these words can you say?

The pictures will help you. Look back in your book

and see if you can find the words in the story.

workbench

shoemaker

money

wife

elves

clothes

rich lady

rich man

shoes